A IS FOR ADVENTURE

AN
ALPHABET MONSTER COLORING BOOK
WITH 26 ADVENTURE SEEDS

SCOTT ALERIC

WITH BOOK DESIGN BY KAT VANCIL

Korat Publishing

A IS FOR ADVENTURE

Conceptualization, Cover art, Interior art, Maps, and Writing
SCOTT ALERIC

Book design, Book cover design, Proofreading, and Editing
KAT VANCIL

Published by Korat Publishing in California
Printed in the United States of America
First Edition

ISBN: 978-1-937288-09-9 (paperback)

The text for this book is set in Bookerly and Optimus Princeps Semibold.

Send comments, questions, and fanmail to aleric@scottv.com

INTRODUCTION

This book of monsters is intended as both a coloring book and an adventure guide. Each monster presented has a long legacy of terrorizing hapless, and foolhardy adventurers—from earliest editions of the original Advanced Dungeons and Dragons game to the more current D20 RPG system, and beyond. In addition to the illustration of each creature, I've provided a description, a map, and an adventure seed. These adventure seeds also include a number of plot twists to spice up the mini-adventure, to make the encounter more interesting or dangerous (or both).

If you wish to use any of these encounters, please do! Yes, this is me granting photocopy rights to you for personal use! As a Game Master, you will need to do a little bit of homework: The bare bones of an adventure or an encounter are here. In some cases, you should be able to drop it into your current adventure with little trouble. Others, you may choose to build a whole adventure around it. This is ideally designed to be used to inspire you to develop your own adventure for a D20 system game, but if you're willing to put a little extra work in, you can come up with your own stats for the creatures to insert into any RPG you play. Either way, let me know how it goes! I'd love to hear from you.

I hope this book offers you hours of entertaining fun and relaxation.

Fleric

A is for Ankheg

An ankheg is a large burrowing insectoid creature, known for spitting a stream of acid at particularly tough opponents, and their preference for horseflesh. A scourge of farmers, ranchers and rural communities everywhere, when ankhegs are discovered, quick action is usually required to save the local economy.

Adventure

The local lord has posted a bounty per ankheg head, and is actively encouraging adventurers to hunt them. Investigation in the village and area will lead the adventurers to the Ander Farm, where the troubles seemed to start. Jebadinko Ander is a gruff, independent sort, but is at his wit's end. First the attacks started in his fields, but they have since taken over his barn. He's been able to keep the anhkegs away from his house, but his situation is becoming more desperate by the day.

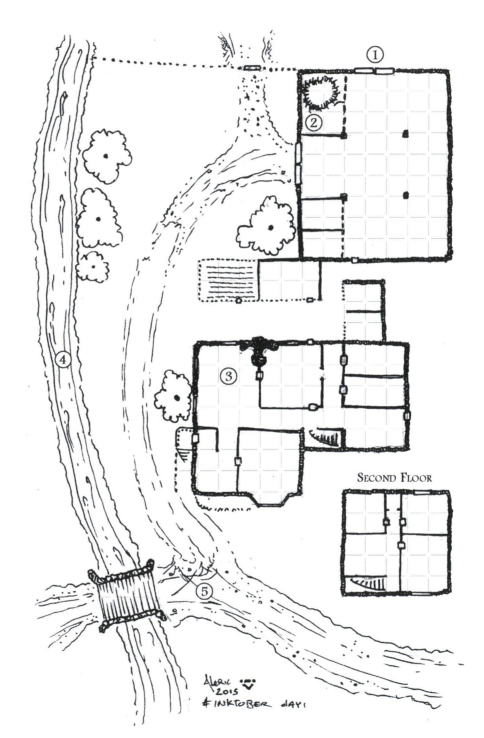

Locations

1. Barn
2. Burrow
3. Farmhouse
4. River
5. King's Road

Twists

◊ Jeb actually has a number of illegal goods stored in his barn, and doesn't want the adventurers to discover them.

◊ A local Druid is in control of the ankhegs, and is taking his revenge on Jeb for damaging some local, rare trees in a nearby grove.

Second Floor

B is for Bulette

Bulettes are huge, ravenous, thickly armored and aggressively territorial. Also known as a landshark, they have the habit of leaping into combat, and attacking with powerful jaws and deadly claws. They are known for their ability to quickly burrow through the earth, the bony ridge on their back rising above the ground not unlike their more familiar aquatic namesakes. Preferring hilly regions, they have been known to savagely attack creatures with no regard to personal safety.

Adventure

The adventurers have been hired on as guards and scouts to a caravan of settlers in a dangerous wilderness. While scouting a route ahead of the caravan, the group is set upon by a mated pair of hunting bulettes.

Locations

1. Dry streambed
2. Stony hills

Twists

◊ A ranger arrives who has been hunting the bulettes as well, trying to collect spell components for a wizard.

◊ The adventurers happen upon the bulette's nest first where they find a clutch of hatched young. If able to secure them, the whole group of young bulettes are worth a small fortune.

C is for Chimera

Part lion, goat, and dragon, the somewhat intelligent chimera comes in a variety of hateful and cruel types. The dragon can sport different colors, with a unique breath weapon for each. Most often the type of dragon also influences the terrain and climate they typically inhabit. Regardless of subspecies, chimeras are evil, foul-tempered creatures that are fiercely proud, but they will submit to, and grudgingly serve, significantly more powerful evil creatures.

Black — Stream of acid — Swamps and marshes
Blue — Bolt of lightning — Desert and arid hills
Green — Cone of acid — Forests and jungles
Red — Cone of fire — Rocky Mountains and hills
White — Cone of frost — Cold and frozen climates

Adventure

Local woodcutters near Woodburn have been disappearing in the forested hills. Some say ettins and hill giants have come down from the badlands, and are hunting luckless peasants; others claim darker influences have caused the disappearances. The town drunks say they have seen beasts in the night sky.

A woodsman tells of a rockfall by an old trail that has recently cleared, revealing a dry stream bed. He believes it may either lead to a better route through the forest, or even to the lair of the ettins he thinks are up there. Either way, he would like some adventurers to explore the area.

Locations

1. Nest — Enough space for a couple chimeras to rest. It is littered with bones, and bits of their previous kills.
2. Pit — Acting as a larder, a couple of missing woodsmen are trapped here, certain their lives will end soon.

Twists

◊ Ettins who live further up the gully are using the chimeras as pets, and guard dogs for their treasure.
◊ The pride of chimeras has young in the nest, and they're hungry.

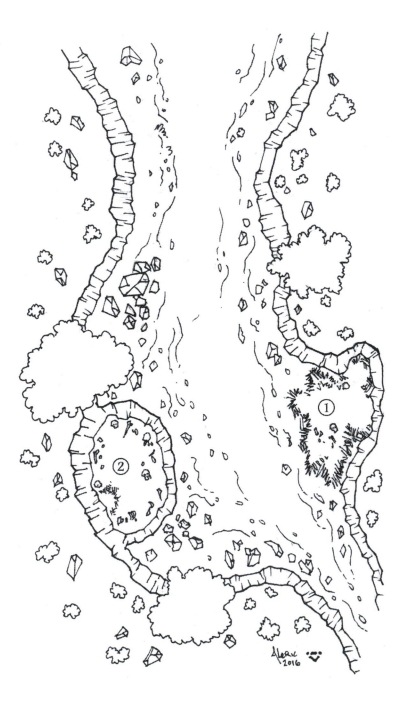

D IS FOR DOPPELGÄNGER

Doppelgängers are pasty humanoids which can change their features at will so they can infiltrate societies. Usually taking up positions next to seats of power, they are able to take advantage of all the benefits without endangering themselves directly. While most doppelgängers avoid conflict and are content to hide among a host society, a significant portion have come to appreciate how their ability to change their appearance can help evade capture or sow chaos.

ADVENTURE

The Sea Maid, a trading caravel has been missing shipments, and the crew no longer responds to letters or missives. The crew has lately become more known for their appetites at local brothels and bars, and the captain has recently turned down a number of lucrative cargo contracts while the ship lies in port.

Local merchant and owner of the ship, Nilson VonCrosia, wants the party to investigate and determine what has happened to the skilled captain and crew.

LOCATIONS

UPPER DECK:
1. Forecastle
2. Aftercastle

MAIN DECK:
1. Crew berths
2. Galley
3. Armory
4. First Mate's cabin
5. Captain's cabin

LOWER DECK:
1. Hold
2. Cargo Hatch

TWISTS

◊ Captain Farinost is actually a human, and unaware that his first mate and much of his crew are doppelgängers.

◊ Captain Farinost is masquerading as VonCrosia to hire the party as crew and investigate.

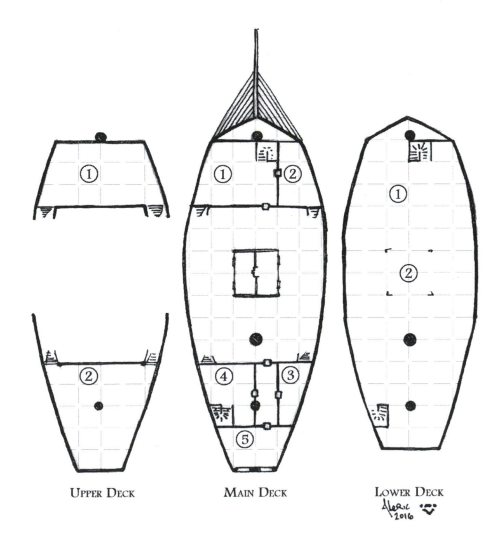

UPPER DECK   MAIN DECK   LOWER DECK

E is for Ettin

Evil, monstrous two-headed giants, ettins are known for their ability to fight wielding two weapons without difficulty. Preferring ambush tactics to gain the advantage in any encounter, once the battle is joined, they tend to fight until they or their enemies are dead. Ravenous and cruel, but not very intelligent, the one thing the two heads easily agree on is when it's time to eat. This natural belligerence leads ettins to be solitary creatures; however, they will sometimes band together under a powerful leader.

ADVENTURE

Ettins have captured a wealthy tradesman from his caravan. The party is hired by the master of the caravan to track the merchant, and kill his captors if necessary. Following the tracks left should be relatively easy, as they seem to show a brutal giant took the tradesman.

LOCATIONS

1. Cliffs/rocky culvert — Ettins will throw boulders at passersby.
2. Front cooking chamber — Ashes of cooking fires with bones, and a great axe serving as a butcher's knife.
3. Lower room — A stream runs through here. In the back of the cavern is a confusing array of shining armor, glass, coins, jewelry, and gems hung in a strange network.
4. Skull chamber — Mostly empty but for a collection of skulls.
5. Prison — Missing merchant is chained to large metal posts hammered into the ground.

TWISTS

◊ Merchant originally hired ettin to ransom him back to his family.

◊ One ettin is a witch doctor, and is willing to trade the merchant(s) for rare spell components.

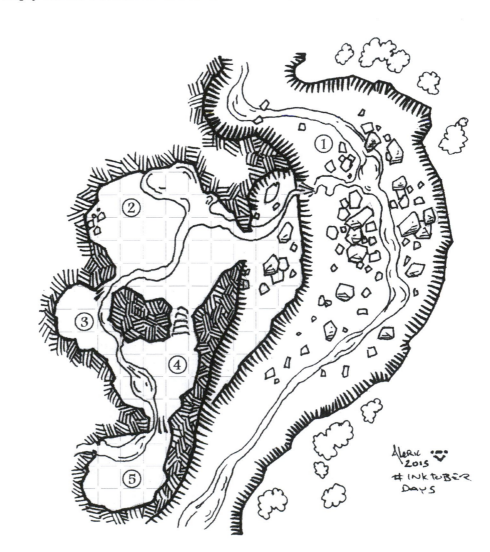

F is for Flail Snail

As big as a horse, the flail snail is known to warp magic cast on it, and sometimes even turn it back on the caster. They are also surprisingly intelligent, but are usually only dangerous to fungi, vermin, and anyone who would attack them for their colorful and valuable shells. In places inhabited by dangerous humanoids, they tend to attack first, just to make sure they don't become victims themselves.

ANY SPELL USED ON A FLAIL SNAIL HAS AN 80% CHANCE TO BE WARPED. IF WARPED, ROLL 1D10:

1-3 Misfire — caster must concentrate for the next 1d4 rounds to successfully cast a spell.

4-6 Redirect — spell randomly bounces to nearest creature.

7-9 Spell fails — spell collapses with no side effects.

10 Rebound — caster of the spell suffers the effect of the spell.

FLAIL SNAILS HAVE A NUMBER OF ADDITIONAL ABILITIES:

Mucus — make a 10ft. x 10ft. area sticky or slimy for 10 minutes.

Suction — climb sheer surfaces, and hang from slimy ropes without falling.

Retraction — withdraw into shell for better armor, but cannot attack.

Adventure

The adventurers have been hired to obtain one of the rare shells by a wizard. A colony of them is known to exist in the lower basements of local ruins. He will pay a bounty for each undamaged shell returned.

Locations

1. Underground river
2. Ruins
3. Colony plateau

Twists

◊ The snails turn out to be gentle, good creatures, and are found protecting an injured creature or child.

◊ The snails turn out to be guardians of a more powerful creature that the wizard is hoping the party will destroy.

G is for Gorgon

Appearing at first to be a large bull covered entirely in plate armor, many are dismayed to learn the fitted metal plates are actually the creature's skin. In addition to using its horns and hooves to deadly effect, it also breathes a noxious green vapor that can can turn living things to stone. Petrified victims will eventually return to normal if subjected to the gas only once. A second breath from the gorgon will make the effect permanent. Gorgons eat stone, using their breath to make the food they actually eat.

Adventure

While traveling across some lonely moor, the adventurers find the area weirdly cluttered with gnawed stone shapes and broken statues of people and animals. As dawn breaks, a gorgon stumbles across the party's campsite and attacks.

Locations

1. Stream
2. Campsite
3. Dry riverbed

Twists:

◊ Stone Giants are in the area hunting gorgons, and may offer to trade, or simply attack the party.

◊ Local gem hunters try to protect the gorgons, as they search the gorgon's powdery mineral dung for indigestible gems.

H is for Hell Hound

Lanky, fire breathing canids, the intelligent hell hounds regularly work together to trap their prey. They are fond of using their remarkably stealthy natures to surround their prey, and drive them toward the rest of the pack. They are often spotted in the service of fire giants and other creatures that are naturally immune to fire.

Adventure

The ruined temple of St. Thomas the Burgher have stood empty for the past twelve years after an earthquake destroyed the monastery. Lately, strange lights have been seen in the ruins, and townsfolk are afraid of ghosts and evil spirits. Normally they would leave the ruins undisturbed, but a few people have vanished in and near the ruins. They would like to hire the party to investigate.

Locations

1. Collapsed tower
2. Abandoned refectory
3. Empty dormitory
4. Damaged statue of St. Thomas
5. Former infirmary

Twists:

◊ A dangerous cult attempting to summon devils for their dark needs have inadvertently summoned the hounds instead.

◊ A follower of St. Thomas came to restore the monastery, but a curse summoned the hell hounds. He is being held hostage by the hounds.

I is for Intellect Devourer

Small, evil creatures that look like brains with four clawed legs, intellect devourers take great joy in killing their victims, and using their body to experience emotions and physical pleasures. They can take over the bodies of a helpless, unconscious, or dead creature by shrinking down, crawling into its mouth and eating the brain. Doing so also gives the intellect devourer its memories to better imitate the victim. In their natural form, intellect devourers are remarkably fast, thick-skinned, and hard to kill.

Adventure

The Naked Cat is a tavern and saloon well known for its ability to provide its customers nearly any sensual delight. Offering space for private events, and discreet rooms for the guests to indulge their whims. Local noblemen have been neglecting their duties in favor of enjoying the distractions at the Naked Cat. After about a week of unchecked spending and indulgence, the nobleman's body turns up in the local river, often mangled almost beyond recognition. Their wealth is often substantially drained or gone altogether. Local officials want to hire outsiders to investigate, as they would not be recognized.

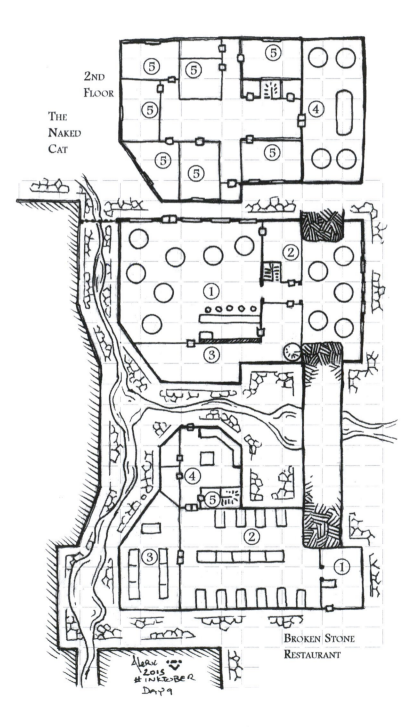

Locations

The Naked Cat:
1. Common room
2. Storage
3. Kitchen
4. Private meeting room
5. Bedroom

Broken Stone Restaurant:
1. Foyer
2. Dining hall
3. Private room
4. Kitchen
5. Stairs to cellar

Twists

◊ A meeting of guild masters is planned for the Broken Stone and for them to later enjoy the Naked Cat, and would likely be perfect targets.

◊ A rival faction of intellect devourers are looking to take over the Naked Cat, and are using their body-slaves to do so.

J is for Jackalwere

Evil, intelligent jackals able to assume human form, they generally inhabit dry, arid regions where jackals are common. Known for their intelligence and ability to hide among people, it is their love of murder and taste for human flesh which people fear most. Jackalweres tend to avoid large human settlements in favor of smaller rural communities.

Adventure

Scattered throughout the land are altars to the god of travel, maintained by any wandering priests and any who vist the shrines. This particular shrine has a small campsite and a well-cared for horse corral. Staying the night will attract a jackalwere pack who attack after dark in hopes of surprising travelers.

Locations

1. Stone hut
2. Well
3. Corral
4. Shrine

Twists

◊ A sickly pilgrim stopped here is found in the hut. The pilgrim is delirious with fever and raves about speaking dogs. If healed, he will fall asleep and awake confused.

◊ The sickly pilgrim is actually a jackalwere that is hunted by his tribe, and is hoping to hide here.

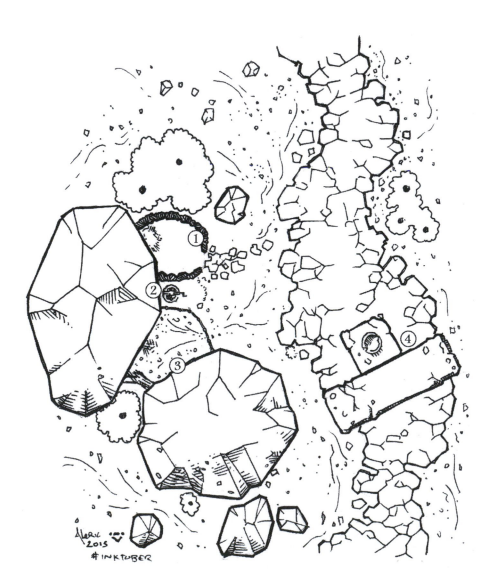

K is for Kobold

Dangerously clever, these small lizard-like humanoids are convinced they are the kin of dragons. Generally cowardly, these scheming, canny, underground creatures make up for their small stature by clever tactics, deadly but ingenious traps, and if all else fails, swarm tactics.

Adventure

These rooms can be inserted into a current dungeon. If not, they can also function as a few rooms under an abandoned ruin that the players have been sent to investigate and clear prior to locals establishing a new settlement.

Locations

1. Outer corridor — The rough surface of the walls here are cracked, and split in several places. Chunks of rubble and broken rock line the dusty corridor.
2. Abandoned chapel — This wide room has a few ancient pillars holding up the old roof, and there is evidence that there was once a fire in this room. This crumbling room may have once served as a hidden chapel, but it is too damaged to know which god it served. The doorway to the corridor has a portcullis withdrawn into the ceiling. Another, smaller portcullis separates you from the far room, where you can see several unopened chests and crates.
3. Once the targets go into the abandoned chapel, the kobolds close the portcullis to the corridor.
4. Kobold archers enter the corridor and shoot anyone who approaches the portcullis, while other kobolds pour oil into the room through gaps in the sides and from the ceiling, and light the chamber on fire.

Twists

◊ Before lighting the oil, the kobolds demand treasure from their victims, to be tossed into the small treasure room.

◊ The kobolds work for a more powerful being in the dungeon, and have been told to capture the adventurers alive.

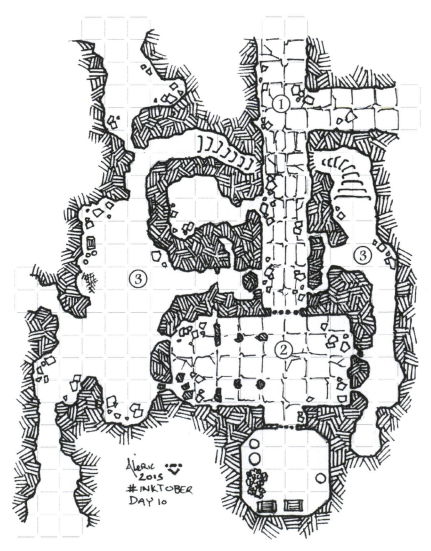

L IS FOR LAMIA

Laminas are race of women cursed to be human-animal hybrids for some ancient forgotten wrong. The most common type of lamia have the lower bodies of lions and the upper body of a beautiful woman with leonine features. Temperamental and violent, they find themselves attracted to ruins and abandoned places. They delight in defiling temples, and harbor a particular hatred of priests of all kinds, using their ability to weaken the mind of their victims by touch alone.

ADVENTURE

A priest hires the party to retrieve a relic from a ruined church, hidden at the base of the altar. Unbeknownst to them, lamias have taken up residence there, defiled what remains of the once holy place, and will hunt anyone unlucky enough to pass through the area.

LOCATIONS

1. Collapsed vestibule
2. Crumbling nave
3. Profaned altar
4. Side rooms

TWISTS

◊ The priest is corrupt and working with the lamias to loot their victims after they are killed.

◊ The item the priest sent for is actually cursed, and the lamias have been searching for the item for some time.

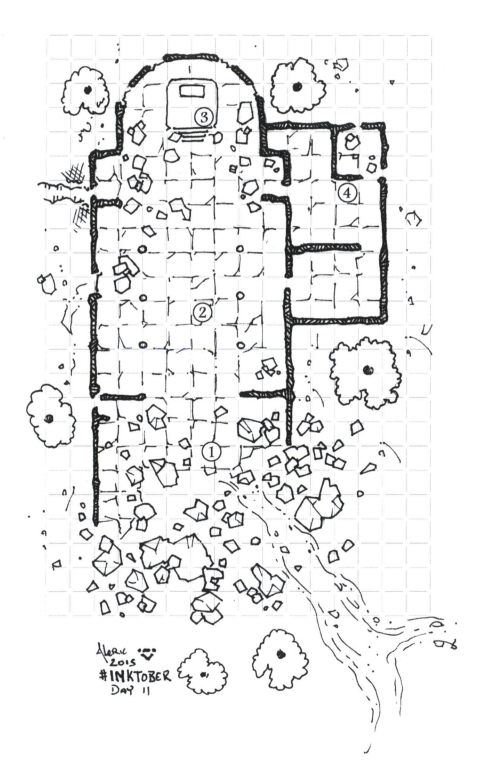

M is for Manticore

Vicious flying beasts made up of a patchwork of different creatures, scholars believe manticores were the successful result of some twisted magical experiment. They have humanlike faces, lion bodies with dragon wings, and either a huge scorpion tail with deadly venom or a tail that can fling dangerous spikes. Intelligent enough to bargain with, manticores are sometimes guards for powerful evil creatures. Having a strong preference for human flesh, they will take nearly every opportunity to feast on any humans unfortunate enough to cross their path.

Adventure

A local mayor or minor noble has fallen ill, and the priests and healers can't seem to cure him without a rare herb that blooms in the nearby swamp. A hermit living there will be able to guide people to the herb, but the swamp is haunted by a pride of manticores, and few dare to enter. The adventurers find the hermit's hut is surrounded by manticores.

Locations

1. The stone face
2. Log bridge
3. Chicken pen
4. Skiff
5. Hut

Twists

◊ The manticores serve the hermit, who is actually an evil ranger or Druid.

◊ The person that sent the adventurers on the quest actually wants access to a treasure hidden near the hermit's cabin.

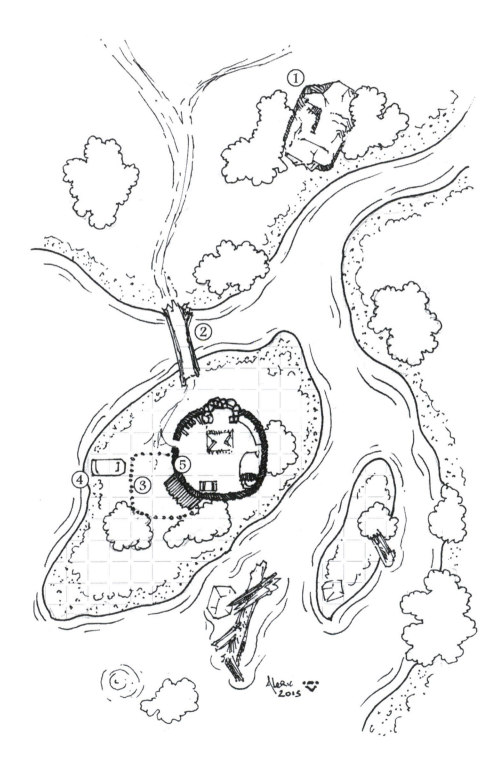

N is for Nightmare

Nightmares are powerful demonic horses that can breathe smoke or fire. They revel in the destruction they wreak, especially when they partner with powerful evil beings who are allowed to sit astride them. Able to transport themselves and a single rider to another plane (such as Hell or the Abyss) once a day, a nightmare is dangerous, but several working together is a terrifying event that is mercifully rare.

Adventure

A dark rider on a nightmare has been terrorizing the area, but was defeated by some adventurers passing through. The nightmare abandoned the dark rider and everyone had thought it wouldn't return, so the adventurers moved on. However, a week later it returned and has been once again rampaging through the area along a well-used trail. The community, thankful for the adventurers' presence, have pooled their money to hire the party to destroy the nightmare.

Locations

1. Embankment
2. Trail
3. Beggar's hill

Twists

◊ The dark rider also survived, and is planning to recapture the nightmare and bend it to the rider's will.

◊ In an act of rebellion against evil nobles, the local community actually summoned the nightmare to destroy them.

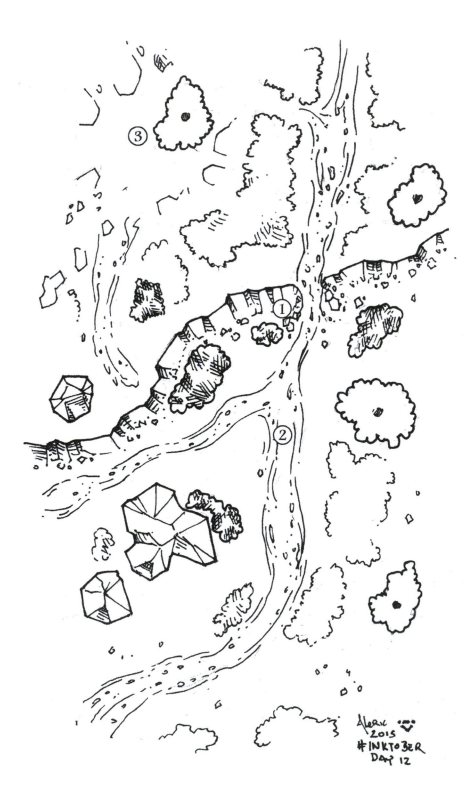

O is for Owlbear

A weird, huge hybrid of owl and bear, the owlbear is a vicious predator that uses deadly sharp claws and its great strength to deliver a crushing hug attack. Owlbears prefer to hunt lonely temperate and cold forests, where its bloodthirsty nature puts a pack of them at the top of the food chain with plenty of prey nearby.

Adventure

An eccentric noble wants owlbears to guard his palace, but believes they must be raised from the egg so that the hatchling will imprint on him. Fortunately for him, a group of owlbears have moved into a nearby forest. He's willing to pay handsomely for each egg that can be safely retrieved before they hatch.

Locations

1. Nests
2. Lair

Twists

◊ The nobleman, concerned over his investment, insists on going along with the adventurers.

◊ One or more of the eggs the adventurers capture is about to hatch, and the noble will not accept young hatched owlbears.

P is for Purple Worm

Massive, burrowing creatures known for scavenging food in the deepest parts of the world, the thickly-armored purple worms are rightfully feared by any who might encounter them. Armed with a tooth-filled maw and a venomous stinger that weakens victims, these creatures are known to easily swallow entire groups of adventurers. While purple worms are known to plague deep caverns and long forgotten dungeons, there are variants that are found in deep lakes or desolate deserts.

Adventure

These rooms can be inserted into a current dungeon. If not, it can also function as a few rooms under an abandoned ruin that dwarven archaeologists have sent the party to retrieve an extremely rare mineral from.

Locations

1. Assembly hall
2. Hidden chapel
3. Abandoned cells
4. Overlook
5. Mineral storage
6. Cistern

Twists

◊ The outpost belongs to a different dwarven clan, and they are unhappy about the intrusion.

◊ The mineral is in an airtight chest and once the seal is broken, it attracts young purple worms.

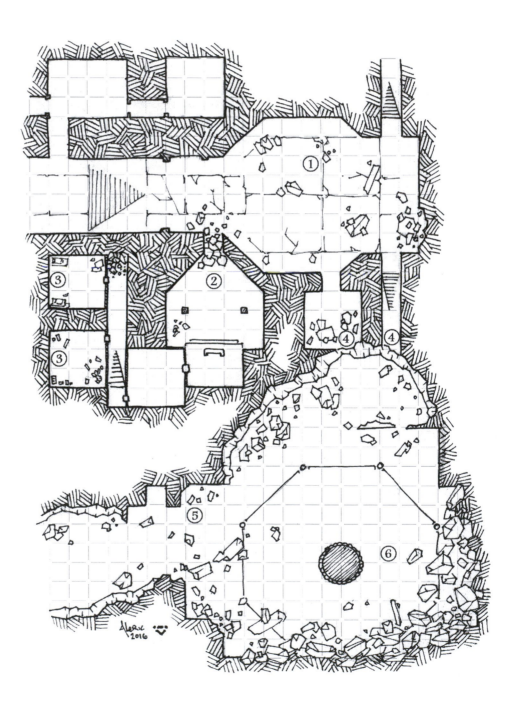

Q is for Quickling

Lightning fast, quicklings are evil fey that delight in tormenting their victims before killing them. When standing still they blend with the background so well they are invisible. When moving, they are a blur that enables them to dodge even the fastest of attacks. Natural thieves, quicklings are fond of using poisoned weapons, are able to cast a few minor spells and are adept at striking their victim's most vulnerable spots.

Adventure

The Gundersen farm can't harvest their barley, because there's something in the field the farmhands have dubbed the "Laughing Wind". So far the Gundersens have lost a pair of farmhands and some livestock. No one has seen what is attacking, but it assaults anyone who goes deeply into the field, cutting them with fast slashing blows, the injuries weakening the victim until they die. The head of the family, Lin Gundersen, is looking to hire a party that can stop this menace.

Locations

1. Gundersen home
2. Tool shed
3. Ancestor tree
4. Kill zone

Twists

◊ The ancestor tree has an evil spirit inside of it that is waking up, and wants the quicklings to destroy the entire farm.

◊ The youngest Gundersen is dabbling in nature magic and will one day be a Druid. The quicklings want to make sure the Druid will be evil.

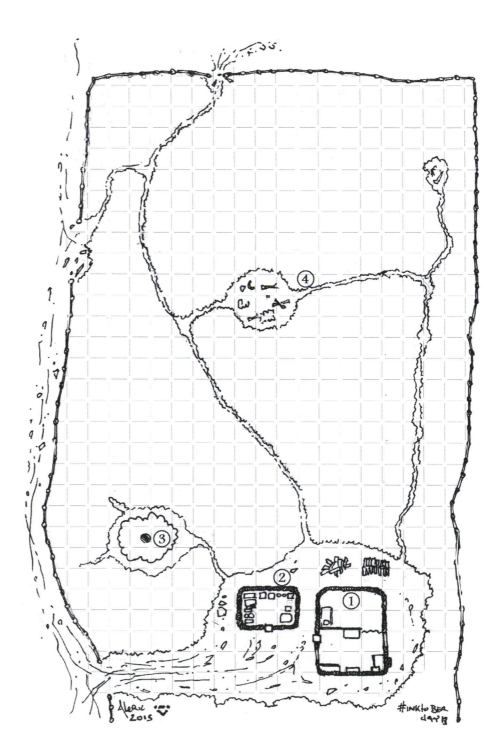

R is for Rust Monster

With a single touch of one of the rust monster's antennae, the horrific insectile creature is capable of reducing any metal it touches to a pile of corroded, rusty metal, which it then eats. The terror of anyone that prizes metal weapons, armor, or even treasure like jewelry or coins, rust monsters can smell metals and usually head toward the highest concentration. In regions lacking in metal ore or refined metals, they have been known to track a potential meal for days. Fortunately, they are not terribly intelligent, though they can be used as mounts for clever, smaller races.

Adventure

These rooms can be inserted into a current dungeon. If not, it can also function as a few rooms connected to tunnels under a city that has been suffering recent rust monster attacks.

Locations

1. Abandoned chambers
2. Ruined cell
3. Lower gallery (15 ft. down)
4. Magic vault
5. Sapper's tunnel

Twists

◊ Enemy spies are using the rust monsters to weaken the city as a prelude to invasion.

◊ A smith is trying to use the rust monster attacks to increase demand of metal items to help his struggling business.

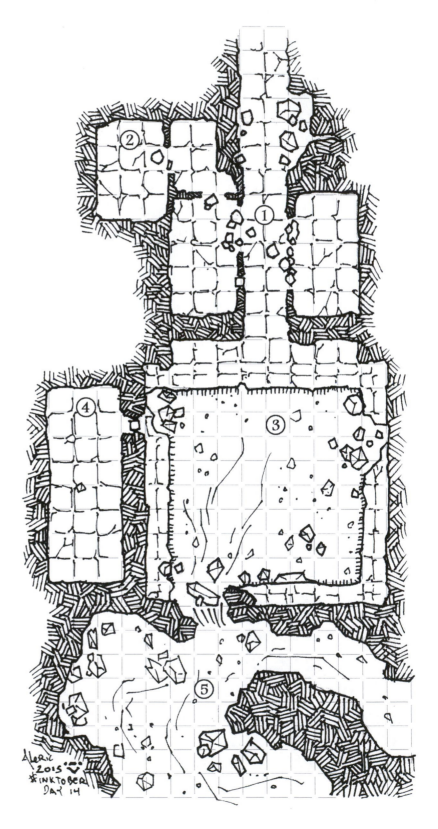

S is for Shambling Mound

Shambling mounds are self-aware and dangerously mobile carnivorous plants adept at grabbing their victims and squeezing the life out of them. Having a strange preference for elven flesh, they are remarkably stealthy in forests and marshes, savagely attacking without warning. Shambling mounds temporarily grow stronger from electrical attacks, and have been observed standing out in storms apparently in hopes of being struck by lightning.

Adventure

An evil ranger has kidnapped a number of villagers, and dragged them into a nearby swamp to ransom them off, or worse. The ranger has left the villagers trapped at a hovel surrounded by shambling mounds, and watches it to snipe at anyone who attempts to fight the shamblers while waiting for the ransom to be delivered.

Locations

1. Hovel
2. Rickety pier
3. Small boats

Twists

◊ One of the kidnapped people is a rival of a local official, and the ranger was hired to destroy the rival.

◊ The ranger is actually a good person trying to let a local "rescue" their love and become a "hero".

T is for Troll

Large, ugly, violent brutes, trolls are always ravenous due to their ability to quickly regenerate nearly any wound they take. Troll's extremely sharp claws are particularly effective at tearing apart their enemies when both claws strike their foe. Their brutal nature and speedy regeneration leads them to be fearless in battle; however, fire or acid gives them pause, since burned troll flesh does not regenerate.

Adventure

A local city has a ruined quarter that was walled off after a strong earthquake. City officials have decided to reclaim the area, but the ruins have become infested with monsters, led by a small clan of trolls. The city council would like the party to go clean out the trolls before their numbers grow any further. They believe doing so will likely disperse the other creatures that follow the trolls.

Locations

1. Prison/troll pantry
2. Bridge

Twists

◊ A hobgoblin that follows the trolls is willing to betray a secret path to the trolls for a price.

◊ Unbeknownst to the city council, a second tribe of trolls is in the middle of a turf war for dominance of the area.

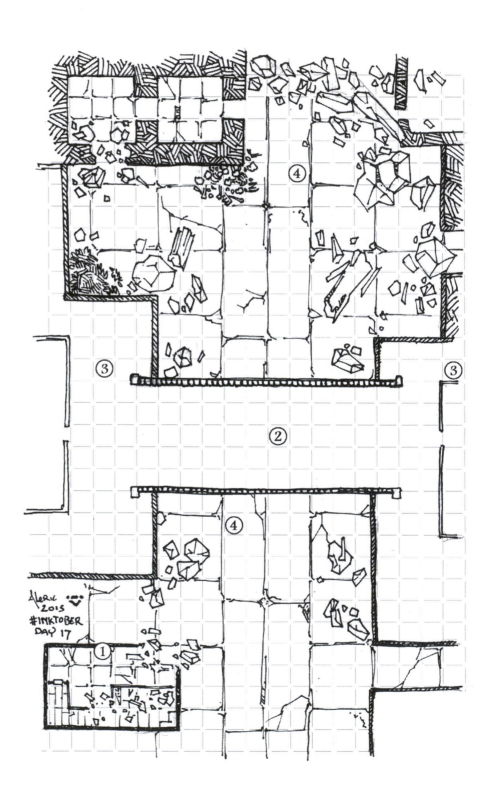

U is for Unicorn

Beautiful white horses of legend, unicorns are known for their fierce determination to defend the good from evil forces, and protect their forest realm. Able to fight with their horn and hooves, they are also known to be able to cure poisoned and injured creatures, and as well as teleport within their forest. Imbued with a portion of their magic ability, unicorn horns fetch very high prices when put up for sale by unscrupulous creatures.

Adventure

Rumors that a unicorn has returned to a nearby forest has drawn a number of evil hunters looking for some fast coin. A Druid who normally protects the forest has been found near death, and is recovering in town. The mayor is unwilling to let the assault slide, especially if their conservation efforts have brought the unicorns back to the forest. Constables want to question the new hunters, and the mayor wants to hire responsible adventurers to search the area around the town for the hunters.

Locations

1. Dryad's rise
2. Shessmyr's trail

Twists

◊ A nobleman is behind hiring both the adventurers and the hunters, with the goal of playing them off each other to capture the unicorn and add it to a private menagerie.

◊ The "evil hunters" are actually naturalists hired by the royal court to investigate what brought the unicorn back to the forest to try to replicate that throughout the nation.

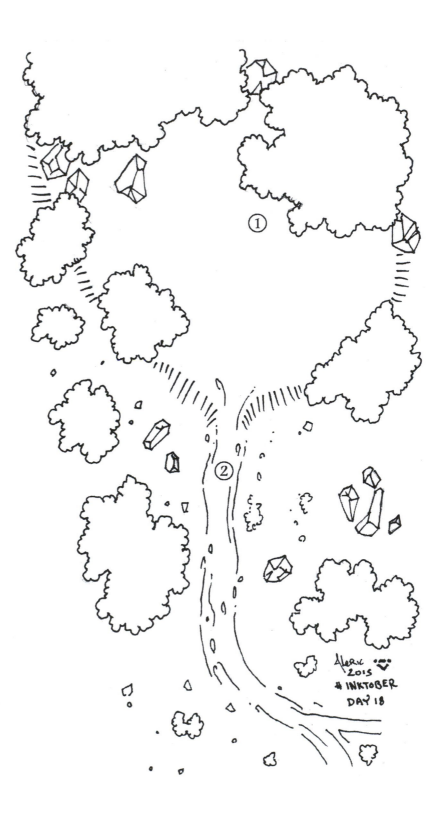

V is for Violet Fungus

Preferring to live in caves and damp, underground environments, the human-sized violet fungi tend to quietly grow in groves near well-traveled passages and intersections. When food is scarce, these purple mushrooms can move about on their own, and hunt for prey. They attack any living creatures they encounter to spread their spores through their deadly, lash-like appendages. The toxin on these lashes causes sudden and dramatic sprouting of new violet fungi in their victims, the rotten flesh dropping off and leaving behind dramatic scars on the unfortunate victim.

Adventure

A village's water supply has recently been tainted by violet fungus spores. Growing on the well walls, drawing water is too dangerous for most villagers, and they can't trust the water they do get. The village needs to hire adventurers to destroy the fungi and save the village. They suspect the source of the spores to be in some nearby limestone caverns.

Locations

1. Hidden grotto
2. Churning pool
3. Lower chamber
4. Upper chamber

Twists

◊ A thriving colony of the fungi has had to search for new prey, because powerful creatures have moved into the caverns and wiped out most of the fungi's normal prey.

◊ A wealthy merchant is trying to drive the villagers away because of recently discovered natural resources nearby, and has seeded the caves with violet fungus spores.

W is for Wyvern

Related to dragons, wyverns are ill-tempered beasts armed with a venomous stinger, claws, and raw, brutal aggression. Lacking breath weapons, their intelligence makes them formidable foes to many who would fight them. Sometimes known to be "tamed", or at least allied with other evil creatures, wyverns tend toward impatience, and rely on violence to achieve their goals.

Adventure

Wyvern attacks have been growing more frequent, and a merchant's secret trade route through some rough hills is being threatened. The merchant needs to clear the area of any nearby wyvern nests to protect his route.

Locations

1. Wyvern cave
2. Nest
3. Miller's road

Twists

◊ The merchant is a member of an evil dragon cult, and has been trying to find ways to feed the wyverns and increase the population.

◊ The merchant really wants a clutch of unhatched eggs to raise a flight of wyverns by hand, and insists on accompanying the heroes to show the way to the nest.

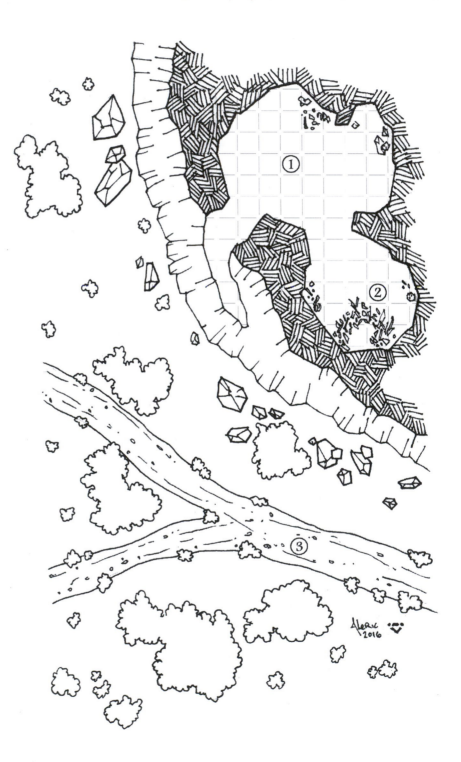

X is for Xorn

Bizarre creatures from the elemental plane of earth, xorn are an intelligent race of creatures with a strange appetite for gems and precious metals. Their affinity for the earth allows them to literally swim through it like water, and can lie in wait for months until the best treat comes along. They are sometimes able to be bribed with expensive gems and jewelry; however, any allegiance gained in this way is fleeting at best. Xorn are highly resistant to electricity and completely immune to fire and cold.

Adventure

An old air temple needs to be tended to, and the local elementalists must perform a ritual to re-dedicate it. However, recent attacks on the elementalists have led them to hire adventurers as bodyguards.

Location

1. Temple
2. Taryn's road
3. Gant's pass

Twists

◊ Tired of the imbalance caused by elemental magicians, a Druid enclave has summoned the earth elementals to attack any who approach the temple.

◊ The elementalists who hired the party are actually looking to corrupt the elemental temple with a blood sacrifice, tainting it with xorn blood.

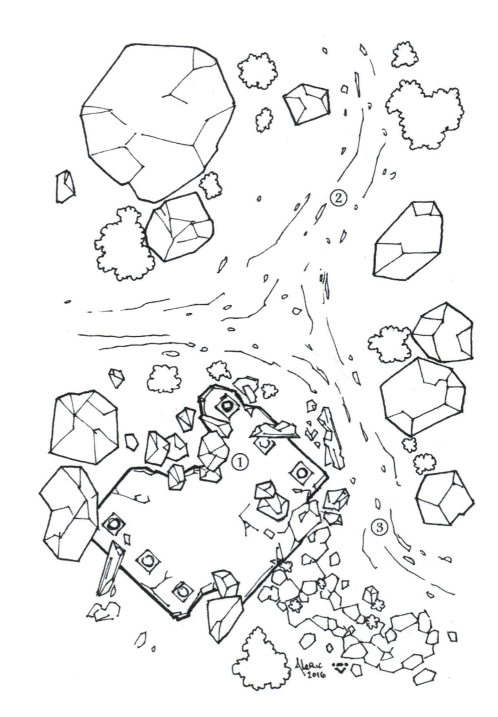

Y is for Yeti

Adapted for the cold, snowy environment of high mountains and the arctic, yetis are immune to cold, and nearly invisible in the snow due to their white fur. Fire hurts them more than it does other creatures, and their terrible gaze can paralyze a creature in fear for several seconds. When found in tribes, they are generally peaceful, but individuals and small groups are often mad, dangerous creatures known for their brutal attacks and raids on lowlanders.

Adventure

The adventurers are asked to deliver valuable, time-sensitive goods to a town on the other side of a high mountain pass. Normally shipments would travel around the mountain range, but this shipment cannot wait. While up in the pass, a storm descends, and the party must find shelter

Locations

1. Fur nest
2. Abattoir

Twists

◊ Bandits are following the adventurers, looking for an opportunity to steal the goods being transported.

◊ Some of the bandits are not actually murderers, and may reconsider abandoning the party to yetis.

Z is for Zombie

The unthinking dead, zombies are usually raised as soldiers or puppets by a necromancer to do their bidding. Not known for their speed, zombies are capable of landing powerful blows on their master's enemies. When left on their own, zombies will often wander the area, attacking and devouring any living creature that crosses their path. Individually weak and resistant to most weapons used against them, they are considered extremely dangerous in large numbers.

Adventure

Bodies have gone missing from a local morgue, prior to being interred. The new school of medical science is suspect, considering the laws against necromancy prevents cadavers from being used for study. Most recently, a few people have been attacked at night by some "drunks". The school would like to hire the heroes to prove their innocence. However, the mortician is actually studying to become a necromancer.

Locations

1. Morgue
2. Cold storage
3. Necromancer's lab
4. Deadman's alley
5. Digger's Board restaurant

Twists

◊ A professor at the school is actually a necromancer using the school for cover.
◊ A cult of assassins are funding the budding necromancer to take advantage of the chaos

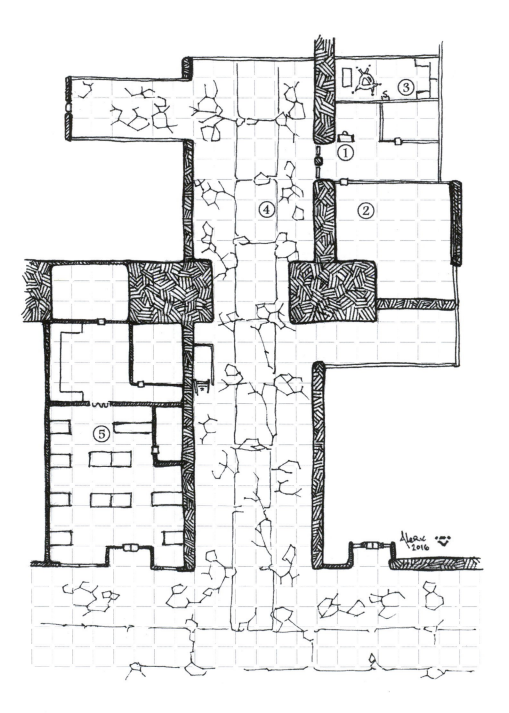

ABOUT THE CREATOR

SCOTT ALERIC has been playing and designing role-playing adventures for friends and family for as long as he can remember. First inspired by the artwork in old RPG books and heroic adventures in various fiction, Scott soon found himself trying his hand at creating his own stories and characters. Over the years, these have come out as epic-length campaigns, countless one-shot adventures, and everything in between.

These days, he continues to explore the dark, fantastical worlds within his head through the creation of maps, art, and adventures which he brings forth for others to enjoy and expand upon.

You can find Scott online at scottv.com email him anytime at aleric@scottv.com and you should check out his work at www.gmatlarge.tumblr.com.

WWW.SCOTTV.COM | WWW.FACEBOOK.COM/SCOTTALERICSTUDIO
WWW.PLUS.GOOGLE.COM/+SCOTTALERIC | WWW.INSTAGRAM.COM/SCOTT_ALERIC